18 MILLION REAL THINGS

150 YEARS OF DISCOVERY AT CALIFORNIA ACADEMY OF SCIENCES

Introduction by Patrick Kociolek
Contributors Michele Wellck, Terrence Gosliner,
John McCosker, David Kavanaugh, Brian Fisher

150 ANNIVERSARY CELEBRATION | CALIFORNIA ACADEMY of SCIENCES

Since 1853

150 YEARS

RICH HERITAGE, LONG HISTORY

by Patrick Kociolek

Previous pages: Collections from the California Academy of Sciences, eight research departments (clockwise from top left): Botany, Anthropology, Ornithology & Mammalogy, Entomology, Aquatic Biology, Herpetology, Ichthyology, Invertebrate Zoology & Geology.

Background: An assortment of species from the Academy's diatom collection.

Top from left to right: *Sequoiadendron giganteum* (Giant Sequoia) in Yosemite National Park; Members of the Academy's Student Section, 1947, examine a frog in their clubroom; Hands-on demonstration, 1997; Meyer Fish Roundabout.

THE CALIFORNIA ACADEMY OF SCIENCES has a rich heritage, developed over a long history, and this volume details and illustrates some of our many accomplishments.

The leaders of the Academy have always been part of the San Francisco Bay Area community. Our founders, among the first arrivals to a frontier town, soon turned their attention to the largely unexplored region that surrounded them, and to the diversity of its species and habitats. Over the succeeding years, the members of the board of trustees, presidents and directors were either already leaders of this community, or quickly became forces within it. These individuals helped secure the resources, provided the direction and oversight, helped implement programs and supplied the vision which has made the Academy remain strong and a salient force within the scientific and educational world.

A tradition of educating children of all ages has long been found at the Academy. Throngs of school children come each year to experience the exhibitions—in any given year every school in San Francisco, private and public, sends at least one class; fully one half of all of the city's school children come here. The Academy also has an extensive outreach program, bringing scientific learning to schools, community centers, and latch-key programs across the Bay Area.

The Academy is still home to the pioneering and innovative spirit.

In the Steinhart Aquarium, the roundabout, the displays of a great white shark and a colony of penguins brought home the wonder of the natural world. When it was built in 1952, the Morrison Planetarium was one of only a handful of planetariums. In the museum, beautiful dioramas and innovations such as the African Waterhole, which took the glass down from in front of the display, allowed visitors to feel a part of the savannah. The Academy, the first home of the Sierra Club, was an early player in the conservation movement. More recently, it became among the first research institutions to apply computer databasing to its collections so that a fuller picture of the region's, indeed the world's, biodiversity is emerging. While our world-renowned research programs have been the intellectual foundation for our exhibitions and education programs, few Bay Area residents know what happens "behind the scenes."

Today, we have a wonderful opportunity to look back over the last 150 years of accomplishments, and to look forward toward our new Academy, that will celebrate and build upon our past achievements while acknowledging the imperatives for the future. The planning for the new Academy demonstrates the pioneering, innovative spirit that we have inherited. We will address the education and research needs of this and future generations, and maintain our place as an integral part of the fabric of our wonderful San Francisco Bay Area community.

Below from left to right: Botany curator Frank Almeda with Malagasy students; Visitors enjoy the inhabitants of one of the three marine mammal pools originally in front of the Steinhart Aquarium, ca. 1923; Caecilian, a legless amphibian, found only in São Tomá; Academy's front entrance, 1995; Red panda in Yunnan, China 2002; Morrison Planetarium's one-of-a-kind Star Projector.

Above: Andrew Randall, one of the Academy's seven founders and its first President. In 1856, he was killed by Joseph Hetherington, to whom he owed money. (Hetherington was tried, and executed by the Vigilance Committee.)

Background: Signatures from the Academy's founding Constitution, in 1853.

THE CALIFORNIA ACADEMY of Natural Sciences was founded in 1853, just five years after the the discovery of gold in the Sierra foothills transformed the sleepy village of Yerba Buena into the robust and rowdy metropolis of San Francisco. Buoyed up by the spirit of grand opportunity that pervaded this period, seven naturalists met on the evening of April 4 to discuss a different kind of wealth:

We have on this coast a virgin soil with new characteristics and attributes, which have not been subjected to a critical scientific examination. Sufficient, however, meets the eye of the naturalist to assure him that this is a field of richer promise in the department of Natural History in all its variety than has previously been discovered. It is due to science; it is due to California, to her sister States, and to the scientific world that early measures be adopted for a thorough survey of every portion of the State and the collection of a cabinet of her rare and rich productions.

Thus was formed the first scientific organization in the West. While other naturalists had visited and collected in California, none had stayed to make it the center of their investigations, nor invited other "scientific gentlemen" to join them in the discovery and documentation of the state's glorious natural diversity. A mere four months after its founding, the Academy extended the invitation to include "females," probably the first such institution in the world to do so.

Left: Proceedings of the California Academy of Natural Sciences, Volume I, Plate 1, Prickle back described by William Ayres, 1854.

A THO

Montgomery Street, 1854. The Academy was founded in Lewis W. Sloat's office at 129 Montgomery on April 4, 1853. Montgomery was one of only two paved streets in San Francisco.

Right: 49ers in gold country.
Below: Mount Shasta.

5

OUGH SURVEY OF THE STATE

Hans Hermann Behr at the Academy.

Top: Interior of Academy's first museum (1874-1891) in the old First Congregational Church building at California and Grant (then Dupont). The mammoth was part of a collection purchased for the Academy by Charles Crocker and Leland Stanford in 1882.

Below from left to right: Gilbert's skink (*Eumeces gilberti*) from Yosemite, first described by curator John Van Denburgh in 1896; *Fouquieria columnaris*, the bizarre boojum tree of Baja California, one of the hundreds of species described by Albert Kellogg, one of the Academy's seven founders.

TION

The fledgling institution had a number of immediate problems to face, including a lack of funds beyond personal contributions and its isolation from the eastern U.S. scientific community—for one, all mail came by steamer, with an overland trek at the Isthmus of Panama. Less passionately curious men would not have persevered. One of the most stalwart members, and the first to have training in natural history, was Hans Hermann Behr. He spoke at least six modern languages, and was called upon by other members to assist them with the Latin required for naming new species. He was also a sworn enemy to "scientific humbugs" and "professional quacks," and so made his share of enemies. He avenged himself on one persistent detractor by naming a particularly obnoxious louse after him.

The Academy's precocious inclusion of women reached a high in the 1880s, when the institution hired its first paid curator, Mary Katharine Curran, later Brandegee, to take charge of the herbarium. Until this time, all the hours and effort expended had gained these scientists purely intellectual rewards. Shortly thereafter, another woman joined the staff, Rosa Smith [Eigenmann], the first female curator of ichthyology anywhere.

Through the nineteenth century the Academy was the hub of scientific activity in the West. Membership grew into the hundreds,

7

Above: Famed naturalist Louis Agassiz who visited the Academy in 1872.

Top from left to right: Ichthyologist and Academy president David Starr Jordan was the first President of Stanford University; X-ray of *Achirus barnharti* identified by Jordan in 1923; Academy scientists G.P. Rixford, W.T. Swingle and Gustavus Eisen.

including "corresponding" members all over the world. Many men with prominent "day jobs" were also active. Academy presidents included Josiah Dwight Whitney, head of California's Geological Survey and remembered through numerous namesakes including California's highest peak, Mount Whitney; fish enthusiast and Stanford University's first president, David Starr Jordan; and George Davidson, known for the U.S. Coast and Geodetic Survey of the U.S. Pacific Coast, and the inspiration for many geographic names from Mount Davidson in San Francisco to Davidson Glacier in Alaska. Renowned visitors to the Academy included naturalist Louis Agassiz, botanists John Torrey and Asa Gray, Lieutenant George Washington de Long, captain of the ill-fated *Jeannette* polar expedition, paleontologist Edward Drinker Cope, and Major John Wesley Powell, explorer of the Grand Canyon. Said Agassiz in 1872:

Twenty years ago, when your Academy was founded, I longed to come across the continent, and perhaps to stimulate and encourage those who were struggling in their efforts to organize a scientific body in a community which was then entirely engaged in gathering gold. My reverence for the Academy of Sciences of California has been growing since I have seen, in your published proceedings, that in a city which is so entirely absorbed in business, you have raised the standard of intellectual culture.

Mt Whitney, California's highest peak.

Left: California Geological Survey group, headed by Josiah Whitney (standing, center).

Right: Marble Staircase and the internal entrance to the Market Street Academy (1892).

Below: The main hall of the Market Street museum.

9

THEN... DISASTER

10

Above: Hand painted souvenir postcard of Market Street in flames following the quake.

Left: George Davidson, longtime Academy President. When the earthquake struck, he rushed for his watch to time the shocks rather than flee the building. He reported: "Marked time from instant of shock 5h. 12m. 00s., hard shocks to 5h. 13m. 00s., slight decrease to 5h. 13m. 30s., reaches quietude 5h. 14m. 30s. First movement N. and S., then E. and W., ending in confusion."

LEAD

Perhaps these sentiments were shared by James Lick, who gave the Academy a valuable lot on Market Street, in the heart of downtown San Francisco on which to build "one of the most magnificent temples of science on the face of the globe." This spacious sky-lit museum opened in 1891 to great acclaim. For the first time, the Academy had a facility deserving of its extensive collection of Pacific Coast fishes, reptiles and amphibians, mollusks, mammals and birds, a rich herbarium, many valuable anthropological artifacts, and a respected science library. Then… disaster.

On the morning of April 18, 1906, a massive earthquake struck. Rather than move their own households to safety, Academy staff rushed to the museum to rescue their hard-won specimens. Using the iron railing of the broken marble staircase for support, they climbed up five and six stories to grab and lower to the museum floor what they could—particularly valuable specimens, a few expensive publications, and the handwritten records of a half-century of Academy meetings. They were only able to save one cartload of material before the far more damaging fire, which followed the earthquake, consumed the building.

But as 50 years of scientific collecting went up in smoke, another small group of Academy men was in the Galápagos Islands gathering specimens that would start the Academy's collections anew.

Top from left to right: James Lick (1796-1876), San Francisco real estate tycoon (and former piano manufacturer in South America), was the Academy's first major benefactor; Facade of the Academy's 1891 building complex on Market Street between 4th Street and 5th Street. The front contained office spaces and stores, and the rear building, connected via a bridge, housed the museum, research offices, and collections; Central court of museum on Market Street; Academy exterior and central court after the 1906 earthquake. The accumulation of over 50 years of active collecting was almost completely destroyed.

Below: Originally built for the U.S. Coast and Geodetic Survey, the schooner *Earnest* was purchased in 1905 and renamed the *Academy* prior to her June departure for the Galápagos Islands.

TO A NEW BEGINNING

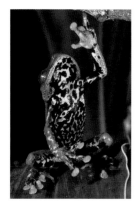

Above: Treefrog found only on the island of São Tomé off the coast of West Africa.

Below, left to right: Albert Kellogg, one of the Academy's founders and first curators. Like many of the Academy's early members he held a medical degree, the only scientific degree available at the time; Painting and type specimen of the violet *Viola purpurea*, collected and illustrated by Kellogg. Such illustrations were important components of a species description, especially before photography.

Scientific expeditions are the cornerstone of understanding biological discovery, and they are fundamental to the Academy's mission. These journeys into unknown portions of the world have become even more important today as species are going extinct at unprecedented rates. Academy scientists have developed new strategies for documenting the diversity of life, and the Academy's expeditions have evolved in their objectives, scope, methods of collection and their emphasis on collaboration.

The Academy's founders had only an inkling of the biological riches that surrounded them. Travel was difficult and much of California was still unexplored. Even Academy members in Oakland lived too far away to attend regular meetings in San Francisco. The state's biodiversity was known largely from collections made during early expeditions by explorers from Europe and the East Coast who spent only brief periods in the Golden State. The Academy set out to change that, and the original forays by the founders were close to their new home. One of the earliest curators, Albert Kellogg, spent much time looking for new species of plants in the surrounding region. While today the wilds of Marin do not sound like a place for an adventurous expedition, it was no easy task to reach Point Reyes at the time of the Gold Rush. The study of Marin's flora has continued uninterrupted, with Academy curators

Schooner *Academy* at dock in San Francisco.

Below: Dr. Edward Ross photographing a damselfly laying her eggs, Napa California, 1969.

13

Galápagos expeditions 1905-2000—Above from top left to bottom right: Ernest King capturing marine iguana (1905-1906); Galápagos finches; H. Walton Clark, 1932; Schooner *Academy* in Academy Bay, Santa Cruz Island, 1906; Blue-footed booby; Live fish for Steinhart on deck of *Zaca* returning from Galápagos Islands, 1932; Watercolor painting by Toshio Asaeda of *Scorpaena histrio* (Scorpion fish), Academy Bay, 1932; Artist Toshio Asaeda with *Opuntia* cactus; *Geochelone elephantopus* (Galápagos tortoise); Botanist J. Thomas Howell, collecting plants, 1932. Howell later bemoaned the fact that yacht owner Templeton Crocker required all expedition members be back onboard for dinner each night, severely limiting how far inland scientists could explore. 1964 Galápagos International Scientific Project inaugurated the Charles Darwin Research Station near Santa Cruz Island's Academy Bay, named for the schooner *Academy*.

Alice Eastwood and John Thomas Howell publishing the first *Marin Flora* in 1949 and Frank Almeda actively working on a revision today.

Academy exploration beyond California began in the late 1880's with a series of expeditions to Baja California. Explorations are still being made by invertebrate zoologists, herpetologists, ichthyologists and geologists. From 1898 to 1899, Academy scientists participated in the Harriman Expedition to Alaska, and in 1903 they launched a major expedition to the Revillagigedo Islands off Mexico to investigate their little-known plants, reptiles, and birds.

The most ambitious and historically important Academy expedition was the Galápagos Expedition of 1905-1906. Professional collector Rollo Beck led the expedition of young Academy scientists (Ochsner, Williams, Gifford, Hunter, Stewart, Slevin and King) aboard the newly acquired schooner *Academy*. The expedition departed on June 28, 1905 and returned November 29, 1906, in such a bedraggled state that they first threw their old clothes overboard "so the Board of Health will not hold us up." They found a city being rapidly rebuilt from the ruins of the great quake and fire. This longest and most comprehensive expedition to the Galápagos produced collections that provided the foundation for rebuilding the institution. In the 1930s, the Templeton Crocker expedition, which brought back 331 live fishes for the

Above: Sterling Bunnell's journal from his 1903 Revillagigedos expedition.

Below: Sally Lightfoot crab, Galápagos 1993, reputedly named after a popular Caribbean dancer.

EXPLORING THE GALÁPAGOS

Top: Inuit tent in Alaska, Harriman Expedition 1898-1899.

Above: Frank Tose and Ernest Hinkley skinning birds on Cedros Island, Baja California 1922.

Steinhart Aquarium (kept alive for months in special tanks built on the ship's deck), and Allan Hancock expedition to these same islands continued this tradition. Today, Academy marine scientists, scuba diving along the Galápagos shores, still seek out new species. John McCosker, diving to great depths in the Johnson Sealink submersible, recently discovered a wealth of new Galápagos fishes. The Academy's deeply rooted history in the Galápagos has expanded as the institution helped found the Charles Darwin Research Station at Academy Bay and the Galápagos National Park. Many Ecuadorian scientists receive training in collection techniques and conservation at the Academy, which also helps develop new exhibits on the islands in collaboration with the Darwin Station.

The first expeditions beyond the Americas were those of herpetologist Joseph Slevin, who explored Australia over three decades, starting in the 1920s. This penchant for worldwide exploration was expanded by Entomology Curator Emeritus Edward Ross, who began his explorations in New Guinea and the Philippines during World War II. Expeditions have since taken Ross and his colleagues throughout Asia, Africa, South America and Australia and have provided the bulk of the Academy's global collection of insects. In the early 1960s, Steven Anderson, a future curator, spent almost a year in the field studying

John McCosker entering deep-sea explorer *Johnson SeaLink* prior to descending 3,000 feet off the Galápagos Islands.

Below: Comoro Islands postage stamp produced in honor of 1975 Coelacanth Expedition led by McCosker.

17

Top from left to right: Entomologist Edward Ross' camp in Serengeti, Tanzania, 1967; Samburan warrior and Pokot goat herder, both from northern Kenya, 1960.

Below left: Galápagos fish paintings by Toshio Asaeda, 1932—
Centropyge passer (Angelfish), Chatham Island (San Cristóbal); *Sphaeroidea annulatus* (Puffer fish) Chatham Island; *Nexilosus albemarleus* (Damselfish) Albemarle Island (Isabela).

ARCHIPEL des COMORES
50F

Expedition to São Tomé and Príncipe 2001—
Herpetologist Ricka Stoelting inspects a
new amphibian.

Top from left to right: Expedition leader and
herpetologist Robert Drewes examines legless
amphibian; Ichthyologist Tomio Iwamoto
admires a freshwater goby *Awaous lateristriga*;
Golden Bush Robin; Invertebrate zoologist
Sarah Spaulding collecting diatoms; Traveling
with donkeys through Gaoligong Mountains
on an expedition to western Yunnan, China
1999-2002.

Iran's reptiles, and beginning in the 1970s, herpetologist Robert Drewes provided a focus for Academy exploration in Africa, where he and his colleagues travel almost every year to study reptiles and amphibians throughout the continent. Last year a comprehensive interdisciplinary expedition led by Drewes surveyed the biota of the West African islands of São Tomé and Príncipe.

From 1986 to 1992 Academy scientists from almost all research departments participated in a series of expeditions to the Christensen Research Institute in Madang, Papua New Guinea. These expeditions surveyed the terrestrial insect, plant and avian fauna of New Guinea while marine expeditions documented the world's richest known invertebrate fauna and accounted for the discovery of more than 200 new species of nudibranch mollusks and soft corals.

These expeditions not only document largely unknown areas but also have a strong training component that brings young scientists and students to the Academy from around the world to receive advanced instruction and pass on their scientific expertise within their own countries. This collaboration with local scientists, a relatively recent aspect for most institutions, has been part and parcel of most Academy expeditions, beginning with the 1921 expedition to Mexico's Gulf of California.

Above: Paleontologists Peter Rodda and Lowell Dingus with the skull of "Tony's *Triceratops*" excavated from Montana's Hell Creek Formation and displayed in the Life Through Time exhibit.

Below from left to right: Expeditions to western Yunnan, China 1999-2002—Botanist Bruce Bartholomew with *Parnassia*; Ichthyologist David Catania and Chinese colleagues collect fish in Nujiang River tributary; Entomologist David Kavanaugh hunts for carabid beetles in Madagascar, 1998; Ornithologists Luis Baptista and Mary Ward studying local bird songs, 1983; Academy associate Raymond Bandar on San Esteban in Baja California, 1966.

Above: Herpetologist Joseph Slowinski with spitting cobra in Myanmar.

Below: Sleeping white-throated oxylabes in Madagascan rain forest.

The Academy's recent expeditions to Yunnan in western China, Myanmar (Burma), the Philippines and Madagascar, sponsored by the National Science Foundation and private donations, have been major collaborations of diverse groups of Academy and local scientists. Few of these explorations over the last century have come without hardship. Molding, bug infested ships were sometimes becalmed for weeks. Rations ran out. Landslides in Yunnan blocked the roads, while leeches were a daily nuisance in Madagascar and southeast Asia. But the tragic death of Joe Slowinski from a venomous snake bite in Burma last year reminded the Academy's scientists that there are still lethal dangers to exploration, even with modern communication and transportation.

Today, when scientists return from the field they must develop a comprehensive view of the evolution, distribution, and conservation of the organisms they have studied and disseminate that knowledge to the global community. This broad understanding and subsequent concern are a product of the Academy's rich history of exploration and are made more urgent in the context of the current biodiversity crisis.

Ranomafana National Park, Madagascar, home to golden bamboo lemurs and a host of arthropods.

En route to the Dulong River in western Yunnan.

Left, clockwise from top left: Udubid spider in Madagascar; Terrence Gosliner in Papua New Guinea's Madang Lagoon which has more than 600 different species of nudibranchs, the highest species richness known anywhere; Brian Fisher with field assistants in the Central African Republic; Charles Griswold with Malagasy students in the Ranomafana research station; Shield bug in Gaoligong Shan.

21

RICH HISTORY OF EXPLORATION

Background: The beginning of the California Academy of Natural Sciences, page 1 of the Minutes from 1853.

Top right: Board of Trustees President Eusebius Molera, 1905.

Right: Scene from the museum's three-dimensional Earthquake Theater which simulates the 1989 Loma Prieta Earthquake.

BEING FIRST IN TIME AND PLACE gave the members of the California Academy of Natural Sciences ("Natural" was removed in 1868) an advantage, but beyond that came the opportunity, the freedom, and often the necessity to deviate from established eastern U.S. and European doctrine or practice and to be innovative.

A few months after its incorporation, the Academy adopted the novel position that "Resolved, as the sense of this society, that we highly approve of the aid of females in every department of natural history, and that we earnestly invite their cooperation." That extraordinary action was followed by the appointment in 1883 of botanist Mary Katharine Curran Brandegee as its first paid curator, and of Rosa Smith Eigenmann, the following year, to become the first female curator of ichthyology of any museum. Other barriers were broken, including the election of its first Hispanic board member, Eusebius J. Molera, who became the Board of Trustees' president in 1905.

Amongst its early cadre was James Blake, a Briton who arrived in California in 1852 and later became the Professor of Midwifery and Diseases of Women and Children at the Toland Medical College of San Francisco. His wide-ranging researches were often published in the Academy's *Proceedings*, and were it not for his innovative approach to

Left: Botanist Sara Plummer, one of the first seven women members in 1878, headed the movement to establish the California poppy as the State Flower.

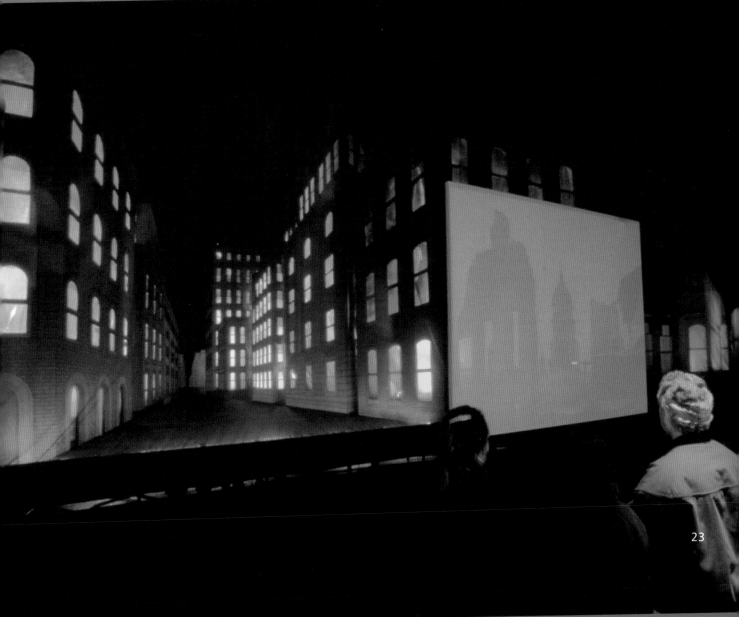

23

A CENTER OF DISCOVERY

BARRIERS BROKEN

CREATION OF ANTIMATTER EXPLORE THE NATURE WITH HOME-MADE EQUIP

FLYERS'

EFFECT OF LIGHT ON BLACK APPLE MOLD

JUNIOR DIVISION
BIOLOGICAL SCIENCES

Above left: Photographs from the Academy's popular, award-winning live TV program, "Science in Action" (1950-1966), thought to have been the first broadcast nature series, and hosted by Steinhart Aquarium Director Earl Herald.

Above right clockwise: Episodes included "High Altitude Survival" with famed explorer Bradford Washburn (1953); 'Science Fair' with winner Michio Kaku, who went on to a prestigious career as a physicist and host of his own science radio program (1963); "Aero Medicine" with test pilot Charles Yeager (1954); "George Vanderbilt Expedition" with the host demonstrating the new aqualung (1952); "Science Fair" with winner, high school student Judy Rupert; "Discovery of Plutonium" (1953) with Nobel laureate Glenn Seaborg (1953).

ecology and enology—the science of winemaking, the otherwise extraordinary soil and climate of California's vineyards might still be producing inferior wines. His painstaking experimentation demonstrated that grapes then in use were too sweet and required more malic acid, via malolactic fermentation, a process that he invented to develop the aroma and bouquet California wines now possess.

Nearly a decade after the 1906 earthquake, the Academy's new museum opened in Golden Gate Park with dioramas representing habitats and large birds and mammals from the West. Illuminated by natural light, they treated the viewer to a dynamic that varied with the seasons and the time of day, a concept new to the museum genre. Later, the Academy went beyond its walls with the production of the nationally syndicated television science program "Science in Action." From 1952-1966, viewers from the Bay Area and beyond watched Earl S. Herald and his guests, ranging from Nobel laureates to chambered nautiluses, inspiring many in the post-Sputnik generation to pursue careers in science. Displays without walls evolved when the "waterhole" opened in African Hall and the ten human habitat dioramas opened in Wattis Hall of Anthropology. Other sensory stimuli were activated when the shake table frightened, thrilled, and educated visitors with a simulated earthquake.

James Blake M.D. (1815-1893)

Above: Audio tours were pioneered at the Steinhart, and publicized with photographs of an "interview" with dolphins.

Top: Frances "Rete" Greeby precipitating aluminum onto the star plate to simulate stars.

Top right: Newspaper heading from 1945.

The Academy pioneered the introduction in 1969 of docent-educators to the halls; no natural history museum had previously taken advantage of such natural talent. During the 1980s, staff scientists appeared daily on the public floor to explain their research programs, complete with slithering and preserved specimens from the collection in a new phase of Science In Action. It was followed a decade later by the opening of a Biodiversity Center on the main floor where visitors are given an in-depth opportunity to explore natural history through a variety of media. Now the standard of the industry, the first adventure in audio-guided museum tours began at the Steinhart. The incorporation of interactive computers in Life Through Time was another idea quickly copied in museums around the country.

During the Second World War, Academy talents aided the allies in innovative ways. G Dallas "Doc" Hanna (1887-1971) established an optical shop in the Museum to grind and polish lenses and prisms, to rebuild binoculars, telescopes, and even periscopes in use by the U.S. Navy's Pacific fleet. Academy scientist Wilbert M. "Wib" Chapman (1910-1970), curator of ichthyology, traveled the Pacific on a classified mission—setting up local fisheries at island bases so that GIs could safely dine on fresh, instead of canned, fish.

Red Stamps Q5, R5, S5 good through March 31; T5, U5,
V5, W5 and X5 good through April 28; Y5, Z5, A2, B2,
C2, D2 valid through June 2. Salvage all fats. Your
butcher will give 4c and two red points per pound.

CANNED FRUITS AND VEGETABLES—Book IV, Blue
Stamps X5, Y5, Z5, A2, B2 good through March 31; C1
D2, E2, F2, G2 good through April 28; H2, J2, K2, L2,
M2 good through June 2.

sued with "A" Book, and thro
cover, writing new number ab
bers on gas coupons.)

SUGAR—Stamp 34 good throu
through June 2.

SHOES—Airplane Stamps Nos.
III, attached, valid indefinite
in 1½-foot bundles for collect

ADEMY AT WAR

27

Above: North American Hall during World
War II—the Academy's precision grinding
skills were utilized by the U.S. Navy for
reparing optical equipment.

Left to right: Life Through Time interactive
computers, another first in exhibit design;
Science In Action lecture on the museum
floor, 1987; Biodiversity Resource Center.

State-of-the-art Star Projector in the Morrison Planetarium, built 1952, with astronomer Leon Salanave giving the first planetarium lecture.

Top: Instrument-maker Albert S. "Jimmy" Getten working on plans for the projector.

At the war's end, Hanna and A. S. "Jimmy" Getten (1893-1968), an instrument maker and the Academy's most remarkable inventor, used war surplus materials to assemble a breakthrough star projector. Rather than being shaped like a large dumbbell with planetary spheres at each end, their projector centered the mass to provide balance and stability. Instead of drilling tiny holes in the spheres through which "starlight" would pass, they used a glass plate upon which grains of carborundum were accurately and precisely positioned by hand. Then, like a telescopic mirror, aluminum was deposited with the grains exposed. After the grains were removed, the slightly irregularly shaped holes released starlight that appeared to twinkle. Nothing except the clear night sky could compete with the Morrison Planetarium. Getten designed the "Reasons for the Seasons," a mechanical device that demonstrated the path of the Earth around the sun. He also invented the Selectro-Slide automatic slide projector, eight models of optical projection orreries, a seismograph display, and a seismic disturbance switch that, in the event of an earthquake, allowed Lawrence Livermore Laboratory to shut down nuclear reactors almost instantaneously. All of these marvelous inventions were created well in advance of computers.

In the Aquarium, such novel displays as a gyral circulating anchovy tank and an eccentric dump bucket (mimicking a crashing wave) gave

Above: Finished star plate with "holes" in it accurately representing star positions.

Below from left to right: Repairing binoculars for the U.S. Navy during World War II; Building the star projector with team head G Dallas Hanna (right); George Bunton and Alvin Gundred working on the electrical installation.

visitors a glimpse of life underwater. The Steinhart was the first public aquarium to install solar collectors on the roof through which its tropical tank waters circulated, and pathologist Robert Dempster developed parasite removal and brine shrimp-rearing techniques that kept fishes healthy and well fed. The Aquarium's Director Earl Herald made numerous trips to Baja California in search of new species such as the blue-spotted, finger-length golden jawfish. Another "first" was the display of flashlight fishes, the brightly luminous, nocturnal deep reef fish Steinhart Director John McCosker discovered while searching for coelacanths. Other firsts for the Steinhart included deep-sea fish, garden eels, soupfin sharks, a dugong and an Amazonian manatee. But the most memorable was Sandy, the great white shark.

We designed the Fish Roundabout as a toroidal tank, shaped like a doughnut, so that pelagic fish, including sharks, could swim continuously through an infinite window of water. The display of a living great white shark had long evaded all aquariums. Then, in August 1980, "Sandy," a great white caught by a local fisherman, was gently lowered into the tank. At first she adapted well to her new surrounds, but she was extremely electrosensitive and reacted to an electrical leak she could detect through the tank's membrane. After four exhausting days and nights, we released her alive back into the Pacific. We take pride in the resultant sea change in thinking about such animals, an attitude that is now nearly universal.

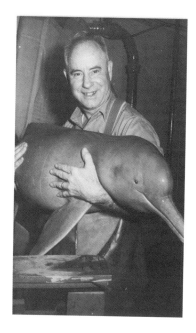

Above: A river dolphin shown here in the arms of pathologist Robert Dempster.

Top: Meyer Fish Roundabout, the first ring tank in the Americas, 1983.

Above: "Sandy" the first great white shark to be kept alive in captivity.

Right: Solar collectors on the roof, used to heat the water in the Steinhart's tropical tanks.

Left: Other popular displays included flashlight fish and "Butterball," an Amazonian manatee.

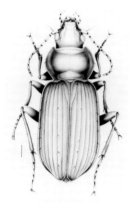

Above: Predatory ground beetle *Nippononebria virescens* from the Pacific Northwest.

Top: Ammonite from Germany, now in Life Through Time exhibit.

Below left to right: Tortoise carapaces and other specimens brought back from the Galápagos Islands in 1906 began the rebuilding of the Academy's collection; hummingbird study skins from the ornithology collection.

IN ITS ORIGINAL CONSTITUTION, adopted May 16, 1853, the Academy resolved to initiate "the collection of a cabinet of specimens and a library to include the standard and current works on Natural History and Natural Science." Within a week, the collecting had begun in earnest. Andrew Randall, the Academy's first president, contributed specimens of granite from China and Monterey, coal from Santa Barbara, cinnabar from Mission Dolores (in San Francisco), and "carbonate of lime" from Sanchez Rancho (now part of San Mateo County). Now, one hundred and fifty years later, that "cabinet" holds nearly 18 million specimens.

The first recorded fish specimen was a California perch and the first herpetological specimen was the shell of a giant Galápagos tortoise, presented in January 1854 by an unnamed sea captain whose ship had just arrived in San Francisco. The acquisition of anthropological materials representing California's native populations as well as indigenous cultures from other parts of the world, began almost immediately. These earliest acquisitions established the future direction of the Academy's collections. They would be broad in scope—including rocks and minerals, plants and animals, and anthropological materials—and worldwide in coverage, although always with a strong emphasis on California and western North America.

Above: All that remained of the mineral specimens rescued after the 1906 earthquake and fire which devastated the collections.

Right: Ichthyologists William Eschmeyer and David Catania with a small part of the collection.

33

8429
S.E. Albemarle Isl.
Galapagos
Oct. 1906

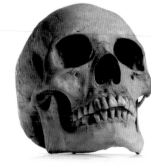

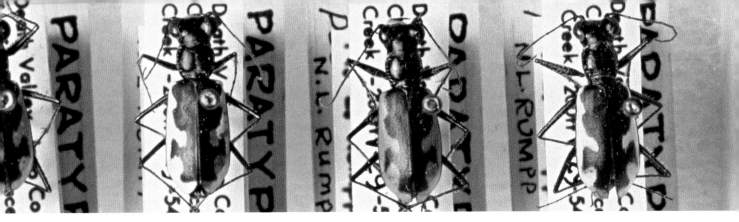

By 1900, the Academy's collections were already large and diverse for their time, estimated to include at least one-quarter million specimens; and its library was acknowledged as the finest natural history library west of the Mississippi. Unfortunately, that was not to last. The earthquake and fire of 1906 destroyed all but the most durable specimens and a few of the most precious and portable plant and insect specimens, which were rescued by intrepid, dedicated curators who climbed through the rubble just ahead of the flames.

But resumption of collecting was swift. Later that same year, the schooner *Academy* returned to San Francisco from the Galápagos, laden with treasures that immediately brought the Academy's collection to a new level of international importance. Even today, these Galápagos holdings, at least for birds—including "Darwin's finches"—tortoises, insects, and plants are perhaps the most important in the world.

Different kinds of specimens require different conservation and storage facilities. The maintenance, use, and development of the various collections is the responsibility of each of the eight research departments: Anthropology, Botany, Entomology, Herpetology, Ichthyology, Invertebrate Zoology & Geology, Ornithology & Mammalogy and Aquatic Biology—primarily concerned with the live collection—and the Academy Library. At present, the Academy's collections include nearly

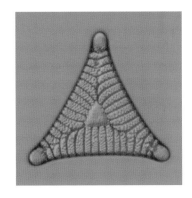

Clockwise from top left: Checking paratype specimens, part of the Entomology Department's collection of some 10 million specimens; Carabid (predatory grounddwelling) beetles. The collection includes over 40,000 species of carabids ranging in size from under 1mm to over 10 cm; Collections range in size from diatoms (above), some as small as 50 microns, to a 100-foot blue whale skeleton (below); Skulls of American alligator, walrus, human, musk ox; Galápagos tortoise eggs.

CULTURAL ARTIFA

18 million natural and cultural history specimens, with a growth rate averaging about two percent per year, and about 6,000 live animals and plants. The Academy Library now includes more than 210,000 volumes, with over 2,700 current serial titles and 25,000 maps. The associated Special Collections include more than 400 archive and manuscript collections, and over 300,000 images.

The scientific and cultural treasures range in size from a huge blue whale skeleton to thousands of microscopic diatoms. Many of them have great popular appeal: beautiful Pomo woven baskets, Hopi kachina carvings, and jewelry from the Elkus Collection; the skin of a Costa Rican resplendent quetzal and a mounted grizzly bear; a giant ammonite fossil, a spectacular gypsum crystal, and a colossal jade rock; a series of brilliant blue Morpho butterflies and Darwin's hawk moth with its incredibly long proboscis; and many historical books, including a copy of the rare Audubon "elephant portfolio."

Then there are live collections. Of course these are transitory and some, such as the two headed-snake, "Butterball" the manatee, the Ganges river dolphin, and the spinner dolphins are no longer with us.

Clockwise from top left: Navajo chief blanket circa 1870; Hopi eagle kachina doll; Magical Moonshine Theatre perform "Tales from Uncle Remus"; Hopi jar by Fannie Nampeyo, circa 1930; "Cabinets of curiosity" in the Market Street Museum, circa 1892; Xipe Totec Dancers perform indigenous Mexican dances; Hawaiian water gourd; Mayan jar circa 14th century.

37

38

Peter Fritsch and Bruce Bartholomew gather botanical specimens in China during the monsoon.

But the coral reef ecosystem, the black-footed penguins, and the 60-year old gars live on.

The scientists who work at the Academy have multiple priorities. Their excitement comes from the thousands of small, black predatory beetle specimens that represent hundreds of species new to science and still to be described; from the sheets of botanical specimens, and jars filled with scorpions, and lizards brought back from expeditions to Baja California and Chiapas, Mexico; from the jars of nudibranchs and sea anemones from the years of Academy fieldwork in Papua New Guinea; from the hundreds of frogs and snakes from Myanmar and thousands of plants, spiders, and insects from Madagascar and Yunnan, China. Each collection is a unique and vital resource to document biotic or cultural diversity and its geographical and temporal distribution.

Such treasures delight both the eye and the mind. From the start, the Academy's goal has always been to develop these important scientific and cultural resources to support the studies of its researchers and those of the greater scientific community. They are preserved here for future generations of scientists and visitors to share.

Above: Cuban Tree Frog, *Osteopelis septentrionalis* from the West Indies.

Right: 80 million-year-old Asteroid starfish fossil found in Butte County, California and now in Life Through Time.

Below: Three of the Academy's collection of over 10,000 delicate nests and eggs.

Every species, like every individual, exists on the Earth for a finite period. Be. Beget. Begone. Some leave no descendents. Others are the forebears of the multitudinous life that surrounds us today. Academy scientists are Nature's genealogists.

41

Above: Fossilized *Knightia eocaena*, a herring-like fish that lived 50 million years ago. Found by David Starr Jordan in the Green River formation in Wyoming.

Right: This frog specimen shows how tissues are cleared using tryspin and then bleached with hydrogen peroxide. Bone and cartilage (invisible before staining) are then selectively stained with alcian blue and alizaran red respectively. This allows for close 3-D examination of structures.

CONSERVATION

PRESERVING BIODIVERSITY

by Brian Fisher

THE HALF DOME.

Above: Carleton Watkins photograph from *The Yosemite Book* by Josiah Whitney.

Clockwise from top: The Academy advocated the protection of Mount Shasta and helped establish Yosemite and its giant redwoods as a park as well as helped breed and protect the winter-run Chinook salmon.

IN THE PAST FEW YEARS, understanding of the term "biodiversity" and its importance, as well as threats to species all over Earth, have increased dramatically. Systematics—the discovery, naming, and classification of organisms—is a major component of biodiversity research and conservation. And natural history museums, including the California Academy of Sciences, are uniquely suited to apply systematic research and education to biodiversity and conservation.

The essential function of natural history museum collections is to preserve, interpret, and disseminate knowledge of species and their interdependence, both past and present. The Academy provides important resources for solving the largest and most pressing environmental issue today—the erosion of world biodiversity. The ever-accelerating rate of destruction of natural habitats and extinction of species makes the task of documenting the Earth's fauna and flora more pressing than ever before.

The Academy has been an advocate for conservation since its early years. It was a strong supporter for the conservation of Yosemite in 1863, the protection of Mount Shasta in 1888, and the creation of Big Basin Redwoods, California's first state park, in 1902. In 1894, the Academy noted the droughts, floods, and famine that followed the

PRESERVING BIODIVERSITY

Jack Laws instructs a Junior Academy class at Mountain Lake which the Academy is helping to restore.

Below from left: Peter Raven, now director of the Missouri Botanical Garden, as a member of the Junior Academy in 1948; A leaf from the Presidio Manzanita, *(Arctostaphylos pungens var ravenii)* which Raven discovered in 1951 when he was 15 years old. Today only a single specimen is known to exist, growing somewhere in San Francisco's Presidio; A Darwin's Finch in the Galápagos.

44

destruction of forests in France and Russia, and sent a resolution to protect California's forests to Washington D.C.

The Academy has a long history in helping to preserve Mountain Lake in San Francisco's Presidio, from publicly opposing the lake's total destruction in 1895 to make room for a highway, to organizing scientists, volunteers, and schoolchildren in monitoring its diversity today. And in 1897, the Academy's members recommended expanding the state's game laws to protect "wild birds," (other than the "English sparrow").

When the Academy launched *Pacific Discovery* magazine in 1948, one of its primary goals was to encourage conservation; Aldo Starker Leopold, son of renowned naturalist Aldo Leopold, was appointed the first conservation editor. The magazine, now called *California Wild*, continues to feature conservation issues and the plights of endangered and threatened species throughout the world.

The vast early collections of the Academy now serve as unique libraries that document the historical presence of species across threatened habitat. They are often the only evidence of change in species distribution over time. For example, to better understand human impacts on the San Francisco Bay ecosystem, the Academy's invertebrate zoologists compare modern sediment samples taken from multiple sites in the Bay with our collections of Bay organisms from a hundred years

Above: First conservation editor A. Starker Leopold teaching on Science in Action, 1951.

Top: David Porrazzo, who later became a Planetarium artist, reading *Pacific Discovery*, 1953. *Pacific Discovery*, now *California Wild*, has been the standard bearer of the Academy's conservation message since it was founded in 1948.

Above: The Dalai Lama makes friends with a black-footed penguin in Steinhart Aquarium, 1990.

Top left to right: Pronghorn antelope. The Academy's Committee for the Conservation of Wildlife established, circa 1917, created refuges for over-hunted animals such as tule elk and pronghorn antelope; Volunteers assist in the SFBay2K project to inventory the diversity of San Francisco Bay.

ago. Similarly, often the only records of recently or nearly extinct species are museum specimens and their associated collection data. In the Academy's entomology collections, several specimens of butterfly species now presumed to be extinct provide the only evidence of their existence.

The Academy is currently coordinating two large interdisciplinary projects to inventory two of the most threatened habitats in the world: Madagascar and China. These projects aim to document and analyze the geographic variation in biotic assemblages within the regions and apply the information to conservation planning. By applying modern analytical tools to our invaluable collections of plants, insects, birds, frogs, snakes, fish and mammals, we can synthesize a relatively comprehensive picture of the pattern of biodiversity in a given "hotspot"—a region of many endemic species under serious threat. The projects are based on the assumption that we can be much more effective at protecting any plant or animal, at a much lower cost, when we understand it. We cannot know the real value of something without understanding it, much less if we do not even know it exists. The Academy's primary role in the twenty-first century is to overcome those hurdles.

Nest of the *Agelaius phoeniceus* (red-winged blackbird).

Right: Mountain Lion from the book *Witness: Endangered Species of North America* by Susan Middleton and David Liittschwager sponsored by the Academy.

THEN COMES UNDERSTANDING

47

Editor: Keith K. Howell
Design: Sterling Larrimore
Lead Researchers: Michele Wellck, Karren Elsbernd
Assistant Editor: Suzanne Ubick
Production: Diane Dias, Virginia Lindsay

Photographers/Permissions

Toshio Asaeda
Roberta Ayres
Alexandra Baele
Sherry Ballard
Rollo Beck
Marc Charnow
Gerald and Buff Corsi
Edward S. Curtis
H. Vannoy Davis
Dong Lin
Lorraine Elrod
Charlotte Fiorito
Al Giddings
Ann Giordano
Terrence Gosliner
G Dallas Hanna
Margaret Hanna
Jepson Herbarium
Caroline Kopp
David Liittschwager
Kenneth Lucas
John McCosker
Susan Middleton
Morton Photographs
Elmer Moss
Robert T. Orr
Robert Potts
Edward S. Ross
Smithsonian Institution
Robert L. Usinger
Glenn Vargas
Charles Webber
Barbara West

Artists

Dorothy Apted
Toshio Asaeda
Albert Kellogg
Jenny Speckels

Research

Alan Leviton
Robert Drewes
Jean DeMouthe
Tomio Iwamoto
Douglas Long
Norman Penny
Edward S. Ross

Published by California Academy of Sciences,
Golden Gate Park, San Francisco, CA 94118
© 2003 California Academy of Sciences
ISBN 0-940228-57-2
Printed in Hong Kong